GOD GIVES US HEAVEN

A story about salvation for kids based on
Romans 6:3–11; Revelation 21:1–6; 22:1–5

Written by Lisa Clark

Illustrated by Emma Gillette

CONCORDIA PUBLISHING HOUSE · SAINT LOUIS

In such a world where butterflies
Enjoy a flower's bloom,
It seems so wrong when someone dies
And rests inside a tomb.

Is this the way that God had planned—
That life would have to end?
It's just so hard to understand
Why we would lose a friend.

The Bible teaches that the Lord
Made all things right and good.
But all went wrong when we declined
To listen as we should . . .

Our God created all the things:
The stars, the fish, the trees,
The angels, people, birds with wings,
The flowers, and the bees.

But God's first people sinned and broke
The one rule He had made.
The Father found them, and He spoke:
"You both have disobeyed."

The whole world suffered under sin!
Now there was death and pain.
Our hearts were dirty from within;
We could not wash the stain.

But God the Father made a way
To make creation new.
The Son of God would save the day
And make sad things untrue.

When Jesus came to earth, He said:
"The Kingdom is at hand!"
He raised up people from the dead
And helped the hurting stand.

The perfect Son did all things well,
Was holy in our place
To conquer sin and death and hell
And give to us His grace.

The Father promised that the Son
Would die to pay sin's price.
So on the cross, our Savior won
With His own sacrifice.

But wait, there's more! Yes, Jesus rose
And nevermore will die.
His awesome resurrection shows
That He is King on high!

Our Savior rules and reigns above
And sits upon the throne.
His Spirit lives in us in love
And claims us as God's own.

Because our Savior lives, we know
That death is not for long.
Our bodies rest and wait below
Until the triumph song.

Our spirits will live on in peace
With Jesus by our side.
All worries end, all troubles cease.
With God, we will abide.

The promise is not finished yet.
Yes, there is more to learn.
When all is ready, all is set,
Our Savior will return!

A mighty song and trumpet call
Will fill the skies with sound.
King Jesus will be over all;
His power will abound!

Both heav'n and earth He will reclaim,
The Kingdom now complete.
And all will bow at Jesus' name
And fall before His feet.

Then all creation will be new
And better than before!
We'll rise again—oh, yes, it's true!
And death will be no more.

Dear Parent:

Children have big questions, even at young ages. These questions might be about heaven, death, where Jesus is, and more. Sometimes, they ask these questions when someone they love is sick or dying. Sometimes, they ask just because. It's okay, even good, to talk about these topics because it helps children focus on Jesus and draw comfort when they need it most. These big questions can be tricky, so here are a few points to help guide your discussion:

- God is wonderful, powerful, and loving. The triune God made everything perfect!

- God's perfect world had no sin or death. When people sinned, death and all bad things came with it.

- God the Father promised that God the Son would come and fix everything.

- God the Son, Jesus, was born, taught, healed, died, and rose again. He did all of this to save us from sin and death and to make everything right.

- We don't have to be afraid to die. Our bodies will rest, and our spirits will be with Jesus.

- Jesus promised to come again. When He does, He will raise us from the dead—just like Jesus did on Easter!

- Jesus will come again and make everything perfect and new—better than before!

This can be a lot to take in. But kids love to hear that one day, their bodies will never hurt ever again. Animals won't bite. No one will get sick. Help them think about all the happy things that Jesus will do for us. Even now, as we wait for Him to get everything ready, we know that He is always with us. He loves us so much that He came to die and then rise from the tomb and go to heaven. And He will come again to make all things new, just as He says He will.

The author